Sailing

the

Seven Seas

Sailing
the
Seven Seas

MARY ELLEN CHASE

Illustrated by John O'Hara Cosgrave, II

A YEARLING BOOK

CONTENTS

QUESTION:

How many seas are there?

ANSWER:

There are seven. The North Atlantic and the South Atlantic count as two, as do the North Pacific and the South Pacific. Then there are the Arctic, the Antarctic, and the Indian Oceans. These together form the Seven Seas.

Quotation from an early geography

"The Sea's a Rough Teacher"

1

MY GRANDFATHER used to say, and very often, too, that, when he was little more than a boy, he owed his life to a cow in Ireland. Indeed, he did, as you will shortly understand. My grandmother, when she was a bride and on her honeymoon, unquestionably owed her life to the fall of a meteor in a hurricane off Cape Hatteras. And since all of us depend upon grandparents as well as parents to exist at all, quite clearly I owe my own life to that cow and to that meteor. Without them, in fact, I should not be now beginning to tell the extraordinary, but quite true stories of my grandfather and my grandmother.

Melatiah Kimball Chase was my grandfather's long and somewhat solemn name; but as a boy he was known simply as Tiah. He was born in the Maine seacoast village of Blue Hill; and he came from a family of sea captains. His own grandfather had followed the sea. His father, Captain James Chase, and his uncle, Captain Judah Chase, had early worked their way up from cabin boys to become masters of their own great square-rigged sailing ships. His four brothers had all preferred the sea to the study of Latin and Greek in the red-brick academy at Blue Hill. It was not at all strange either to him or to his parents and neighbors when at sixteen he stoutly rebelled against his books and begged to be allowed to go to sea like the others of his family.

For young Tiah, like countless boys born and reared in New England seaports, found the docks and the shipyards, the wharves and the piers of his native village far more exciting than any schoolroom and the stories of sailors far more real than any of those contained within the covers

of books. Nearly one hundred and twenty years ago, when he was sixteen, he could see, from his school bench and desk, white, wind-filled sails cutting the distant horizon where sky and open sea met. He could hear, above the voice of his teacher and the dreary hum of his schoolmates reciting their lessons in unison, the creak and groan of heavy wagons or sleds carrying great logs and timbers toward the docks. And in the spring through the open windows came the thud of mallets and sledge hammers, the rattling of derrick chains, the cries of workmen, and the quick, stern orders of the foremen who commanded the gangs of laborers in the busy shipyards. Once school was mercifully out, he would rush pell-mell with all his friends down the steep hill toward the shore.

The only trouble on the shore was that there were far too many things to see, to do, and to hear. He might watch the stout oaken keel of one ship being laid, or the towering mainmast of another being lowered into place while men shouted, or sang some song which gave them rhythm for their slow, careful work. He might perhaps — a proud moment for him! — be asked to hold a measuring rod, or the end of a plank which was being eased into place on a wide deck, or to carry a bucket of smoking tar to a calker at work on the seams. He would surely hear news thrilling to his ears — perhaps about his uncle's ship, the *Mary Kimball*, long overdue on her voyage from China; perhaps about his friend, Tom Parker, who, rumor said, had been stabbed in Singapore by a knife called a *kreese* in the Malay tongue; perhaps about pirates in the Carribbean and their evil venturings forth to board all manner of ships in search of booty and with calm intent to kill as well as to raid.

For nearly every day some Blue Hill captain who had sailed his laden ship safely in to the Derby Wharf at Salem, or to the Central or the India Wharf at Boston, or to some other busy wharf in Baltimore or in New York, or an officer, or a young supercargo, or an ordinary seaman would arrive home by a lesser coast vessel for a few days' leave before setting forth again to the uttermost parts of the earth and the sea. These men and boys always brought' tidings of home ships which they had met and hailed in open ocean or seen at anchor in faraway harbors, London or Liverpool, Calcutta or Valparaiso, Honolulu or Rio de Janeiro; and everyone in Blue Hill hung upon their words in those days when telegraphs and cables were unknown, to hear these tidings, good or bad, about those near and dear to them.

Tiah did not meet that Irish cow who saved his life until he had been at sea for some six years. He shipped as did all boys of his age as the lowest member of a crew, a mere cabin boy. These boys, for there were often two or more on a ship and usually from fourteen to sixteen years old, waited on the officers; helped the cook in the galley; carried the buckets of food from galley to forecastle where the ordinary seamen ate; raced from stern to bow with messages; grew familiar with sails, lines, and ropes and the ways of each in all kinds of weather; learned to scramble up the rigging onto the yards whenever the sails must be trimmed; grew familiar with ship's time by bells rather than by clocks; and even began to stand their watches like the seamen or to act as helmsman in fair weather, holding the wheel to keep the ship steady on her course. They learned to take curt and even rough commands from the ship's officers, and, above all else, to obey the roughest teacher of all in their new life, the sea itself.

By the time he lay in that cow's crib on a starved and rocky island off the Galway coast of Ireland, Tiah had learned a great deal about ships and their ways. He had sailed to far places and learned more than any geography book could ever teach him: about Cape Horn, which the sailors called "Cape Stiff" because of its mighty winds and storms; about the Mediterranean with its blue water and its countless islands; about Baltic icebergs and the bitter cold of night watches beneath blazing stars; even about the strange-mannered people of Chinese and East Indian ports and harbors. And as he had learned from his eyes and ears about these places and their peoples, he had studied aboard his ship those things which were necessary to know in order to rise from a cabin boy's bunk to a lesser officer's berth: latitude and longitude; winds, currents, and courses; the meanings of a ship's charts; navigation and the instruments which furthered its knowledge. Step by step he mastered each, for he had his mind firmly set on swift advancement in his chosen profession; and he knew what well-merited praise meant when it was brought ashore by captains and first officers and told to the merchants who owned the great shipping companies and many of the ships themselves.

When he had reached his nineteenth birthday, he had won his third mate's papers; before his twentieth had arrived, he was already a second officer, or mate. Nor was his quick rise unusual. Many New England boys who had the sea in their blood and were ready to take with spirit and endurance the hardships which it demanded were masters of ships by the time they were twenty-one. Indeed, there are true and stirring stories in our seafaring history of great ships ably mastered by boys of nineteen and officered by other boys of much the same age.

In January of the year 1847 (and what a fateful year it was to prove to young Tiah, now known as "Mr. Chase" to the seamen taking his orders, or often only as "Mister") he joined as her first mate a ship called the *Sarah E. Snow*. She sailed on January 3 from New York bound to Galway, Ireland, with a cargo of grain for the Irish, already suffering from the beginning of their great famine because of the failure of their potato crops. Although the *Sarah E. Snow* was owned by a Boston firm, she was mastered by a Blue Hill captain and manned by a Blue Hill crew of twenty-nine men. She was a stout ship; but a heavy gale from the southwest, which struck her on the morning of January 24, when she was but sixty miles off the Irish coast, brought about her tragic fate. Towering seas which arose with little or no warning knocked her on her beam ends and instantly drowned the sailors who formed the watch. My grandfather, who was with the captain in the captain's cabin when the sea struck, succeeded in freeing himself from the rush of water; but, try as he did, he could not save the captain. The master of the ship and all his officers and men, except young Tiah, were drowned, overwhelmed

by the waves at their posts or swept overboard by the mountainous seas thundering across the decks. One of the officers, the second mate, was my grandfather's brother, Jim.

"In half an hour," my grandfather wrote in the letter which some weeks later he sent to the owners of the *Sarah E. Snow,* "I was left alone."

Finally, in desperation he succeeded in lashing himself to the quarterdeck rail, and for four days without food or water he drifted with the water-logged, drifting, mastless wreck. At daylight on January 28 he saw land about five miles away, the surf-beaten, rocky coast of some island unknown to him. He was by this time ill from fever, bitterly cold, and hungry; half unconscious and yet aware that the breakers dashing themselves against the island cliffs and boulders must bring his own delayed fate.

But on the island, only four miles from Galway, were some brave, if hungry, peasants, who, seeing the remains of a ship being driven shoreward with a man or boy bound to the railing of her quarterdeck, launched a rude boat and rescued him in the very nick of time. The *Sarah E. Snow* struck the rocks only a few minutes later and gave up what remained of herself to the heavy seas.

My grandfather was taken to the small stone house of one of the few inhabitants of the island, a house sheltering both the family and their animals. He was placed for warmth in the crib of the family cow, a kind creature, he always said, whose warm breath above him saved his life during three weeks of fever. Her owners did what they could for him, sharing their few blankets, their watery porridge, and their coarse bread and spending hours cheerfully in caring for their sick stranger, who was for some days quite unable even to tell them who he was. He and the cow became close friends, he said. As he slowly grew better, he would raise his hand in the cold darkness of the night to feel her warm mouth just above him. When he was able, he was taken across the four miles of sea to Galway, where the American consul provided him with clothes and gave him money to return home by the first sailing packet out of Liverpool bound for New York, thence in early April to ship to Blue Hill on a Maine schooner.

By dramatic coincidence young Tiah reached Blue Hill just in time to attend a service held in respect and memory for those twenty-nine men and boys who had lost their lives on the disastrous voyage of the *Sarah E. Snow*. There, in the church, as he turned to face the choir singing from the back gallery, his eyes met the admiring gaze of one of the singers, a girl dressed in pink calico and a poke bonnet with pink roses beneath its brim. This girl was my grandmother, Eliza Ann Wescott. Her poke bonnet and her round blue eyes, filled with admiration and pity, proved at once fatal to the sole survivor of that wreck off the Galway coast!

Eliza Ann Wescott did not come from seafaring stock. She was, instead, born and reared on a farm in the hills a few miles north of Blue Hill village. The sea had always spelled romance and adventure to her rather than danger. And perhaps that conception of it was fortunate as she fashioned her trousseau in her father's farmhouse and dreamed her dreams of seeing strange places which had hitherto been but enticing names to her.

She was married to my grandfather just two years after she had sung at his "funeral service" and in the same Blue Hill church. She wore a dress, which she had made herself, of pearl-gray silk striped in rose; and, although she secretly longed for a hat with an ostrich plume, she acceded to my grandfather's sole request concerning her wedding costume and wore a gray silk poke bonnet with a wreath of pink roses underneath the brim. Nor was she married to a mere first officer! In the two years since he had lain in that Irish cow's crib, young Tiah had been steadily making his own dreams come true. He was now *Captain* Melatiah Kimball Chase, master of his own ship, which had been built and launched in the yards and from the docks of Blue Hill and which he had christened *The Bride* in the fervor of his new love and hope.

The Bride had been chartered by a New York firm of merchants who put up the money to send her forth upon a long voyage. She would sail first to Bermuda with five hundred tons of flour, and thence with a mixed cargo to Liverpool. From Liverpool she would round the Cape of Good Hope, bound for Calcutta with British goods, from whence she would sail, laden with Indian cottons, past the many islands and through the perilous straits of the Indian Ocean up the coast of China to Shanghai. From there, after some exciting weeks of oriental sights and sounds, she would proceed across the Pacific with five hundred tons of tea and rice for California, where the gold rush was on; and finally to end what was likely to be a voyage of many months, or perhaps even a year and more, she would load with hides for the busy Massachusetts shoe factories and round Cape Horn for Boston and home.

Eliza Ann Wescott Chase was destined not to

see Liverpool or Calcutta, Shanghai or San Francisco on her honeymoon. And her entrance even into the port of St. Georges, Bermuda, took place under circumstances beyond her wildest and most fearful imaginings. After but four days at sea *The Bride*, somewhere off Cape Hatteras, dreaded always for its storms, was struck by a hurricane, which rose suddenly, without sufficient warning for the taking in of sails. At five o'clock one morning Eliza Ann at her husband's command hurriedly arrayed herself in a sailor's pea jacket and trousers. Then she was carried on the careening, wave-washed deck of *The Bride* and bound to a mast of the wallowing, capsized ship.

There she stayed from Tuesday morning until the dawn broke on Thursday, forty-eight black hours of frightful suffering from cold and hunger, from the mighty seas which soon tore away her clothing and beat upon her naked body, and, worst of all, from the anguish of terror. She heard the sailors who had had time to lash themselves to anything strong and stable on the tossing wreck screaming alike their curses and their prayers as the endless hours followed one another in the darkness and the tumult of the storm. She knew without being told that her husband and his officers were listening with practiced ears to the creaking and groaning of their doomed ship, to the cracking and falling of spars as the wind and waves increased in violence. Long before the lights of an approaching British ship lent them a measure of hope, her fears of death had given

place almost to a desire for it.

Then, while the British ship lay to in the early dawn, not daring to launch her boats until the day had fully broken, there came that miracle of the meteor. When I was a child, I always pictured the meteor as a gigantic ball of red fire, somehow suspended in the sky above my grandfather's ruined vessel. Indeed, I felt a bit disappointed upon learning that it was instead a

strange, bright glow in the heavens and over the sea, an appearance not unusual in southern waters. By its light it enabled the British captain to drop his boats over the side and to take off the survivors of *The Bride*, which but an hour later was swallowed by the sea.

My grandmother's arrival in Bermuda was hardly that of a radiant girl on her honeymoon. All the articles of her trousseau, fashioned with such pride and care, drifted somewhere in the wastes of the Atlantic. Dressed now in a British sailor's pea jacket and trousers and ill from exposure and terror, she was helped off the British ship by its captain and my grandfather. She had nothing whatever which she could call her own except her husband, her life, and her gratitude.

Anyone might well have thought that she had already received quite enough from the sea and its rough teaching. Not at all! Like many another girl of her generation she had chosen to marry a sailor, for better or for worse; and she had no other idea in her mind than to stay by him wherever he might go and at whatever cost.

In less than a year, helped out by insurance money and unquenchable determination, my grandfather had yet another ship, this one called the *Eliza Ann Chase*, and my grandmother yet another trousseau. For eleven years they sailed across many seas to a hundred ports and harbors. A ship, indeed, became their home. It was the home, too, of their two children, who studied their schoolbooks in its cabin and in good weather played their tag and hide-and-seek on its wide decks.

So natural did the sea become to them as their own particular environment that they felt odd and out of place whenever they returned home for brief sojourns between their father's voyages. A bed which did not rock them to sleep; a table upon which dishes did not slide and clatter; people who spoke but one language and had skin of but one color; storms which were gentle and harmless and which no one feared; fields and hills which, anchored securely to the earth, were safe and stable — these seemed far more curious to them than did the wide, tossing fields and hills of the sea upon which they slept and played and studied. They watched for distant sails, which meant their only human neighbors, and waited with excitement for the first sight of some new land — for the hills behind San Francisco, perhaps, or for a lonely surf-swept island, whose green palm trees and low white beaches told them that they were nearing the tropics.

Our American Sailing Ships:
Their Voyages and Their Cargoes

2

THERE WERE many hours during those eleven years when Captain Melatiah Chase thanked his lucky stars that he had been born just in time to share in the greatest era known to American sailing ships. Often as he paced his quarterdeck at night under the actual blazing stars of southern seas or looked proudly aloft at his wide white sails, filled with the fair-weather trade winds and bearing his ship swiftly and safely toward her far destination, he lived over again his life since he had thrown aside his books, packed his blue sea chest, and set forth upon the watery ways of his seafaring ancestors. Knowing that his wife and his two little daughters were safely asleep in their narrow berths and that everything aboard the *Eliza Ann Chase* was going just as it should, he had plenty of time to be grateful for his past, to rejoice in his present, and to look forward to his future.

He had been just sixteen in the year 1840 when he first shipped "before the mast," that term used in the language of the sea for ordinary seamen. In the twenty years following that date American sailing ships were destined to reach their full glory, both in their construction and in the voyages which they made to the farthest corners of the earth. They were not as yet doomed to die before the inroads of the steam-ships, although even now in the early 1850's the crew of the *Eliza Ann Chase* would sometimes sight in mid-ocean and even overhaul before a fair wind some small, wallowing, steam-driven vessel crossing from Liverpool to New York under the flag of the new Cunard Line. When they saw her surrounded by wreaths of black smoke, her side paddles plowing the waves, her

few sails helping out her rumbling boilers, Captain Chase, his wife, and daughters would look with scorn upon her, thinking her but a sorry sight in comparison with a sailing ship like their own. They could not have believed for a moment that steamships before half a century had passed would drive sails from the seas and send the ships which so proudly bore them either to rot upon a hundred beaches or to be made over into heavy barges for lake or harbor traffic. The young master of the *Eliza Ann Chase* often said to his officers that Mr. Samuel Cunard was but a reckless adventurer to sink good money in such a mad enterprise. Had anyone prophesied in his hearing that the day would come when Cunard steamships should cross the Atlantic in less than six days, he would have called such a prophet even more mad than Mr. Samuel Cunard himself. For sail clearly ruled the seas in those triumphant twenty years before the American Civil War. Every day from the port of Boston alone, to say nothing of the bustling wharves and piers of New York, Philadelphia, Baltimore, Savannah, and New Orleans, some fifteen ships made their safe landings or set forth outward bound; and young Captain Chase was proud to be the master and the owner of one of them.

The captain of an American sailing ship, whether he commanded a brig bound for Canton in the China trade, or a stately East Indiaman off for the Indian Ocean and the products of Java and the Celebes, or a clipper braving the storms off Cape Horn to make a rapid passage to San Francisco with men frantic after California gold, was second to no man, whatever his walk of life.

Indeed, he recognized no superiors in the American society of his day. He might not have the book-learning of the clergyman, the college professor, the lawyer, or the doctor; but he possessed other qualities quite as valuable for his country's prestige and welfare. He had, in most cases, worked his way up from cabin boy to captain and learned the invaluable lesson of how to take commands as well as how to give them. He was daring and resourceful, enterprising and ambitious. That he was face to face with danger on every voyage which he undertook, only added to his initiative and courage. He expected ill luck as well as good and knew how to cope with both. He understood men and how to deal with them, whether they were common seamen or his young officers, eager themselves, as he had been, for their own advancement. He learned the ways of foreign ports and peoples, grew accustomed to strange languages, and often even mastered the helpful rudiments of many of them. What he had missed from the books which he had thrown aside, he learned from the things which he heard and saw. He may have refused to study his Latin and his Greek; but if his ship sailed to Naples he might well journey to Pompeii to look upon the Roman ruins there, still being excavated during those sailing years. And if he sailed to Greece he could see for himself the glories of the ancient temples. Thus he learned more than a little about older civilizations from experience rather than from the schools; and he took pride in being a gentleman, even though he was not a scholar.

Not long ago in one of my grandfather's log-books in which he set down his records of a voyage to the Mediterranean in 1854, I found this entry:

> It being a fair evening, my officers and I took our seamen, all State of Maine boys and men, from the port of Piraeus into the city of Athens to view the Parthenon by moonlight.

Most young sea captains were not above material ambitions also. Freight rates were generous in those years when foreign trade was at its height; and a careful, yet venturesome ship-master made tidy profits for himself at the close of each successful voyage. With these secure in some bank or invested safely in some shipping firm, he could dream, and, indeed, he did, of leaving the sea while he was yet fairly young, of building a fine house for himself in Boston or Salem, or in some Maine coast town, and of becoming a shipowner or a merchant with far-flung commercial interests. He could picture such houses, having seen them on Chestnut Street in Salem, or on Beacon Street and Louisburg Square in Boston, or beneath the elms of Maine villages, such as Wiscasset or Belfast, Searsport or Thomaston, Calais or Blue Hill.

Young Captain Chase dreamed such dreams as he bent over his charts and logbooks, gave his orders to his officers, or walked about his decks with his wife and daughters. He liked, too, to look back upon the past two hundred years which had made possible his own stirring time and place. Like boys and young men of today who, bent on science as a profession, become familiar with the work of all great scientists from Galileo to Edison, or, fired with the desire to become engineers, learn of the men who built our railroads and dammed our great rivers, so he knew about those seafarers of former days who had been his forerunners, realizing that their daring and ambition had brought about these matchless years in which he sailed.

He knew that long before the Pilgrims came to Plymouth in 1620 there had been sailors from many countries of Europe venturing to the eastern shores of North America. These hardy, reckless navigators for fully fifty years before the *Mayflower* set forth had sailed their small ships across the Atlantic after the fish which swam in countless millions off Newfoundland and the coasts of Maine and Massachusetts. In vessels not more than fifty feet long and able to carry only thirty to fifty tons of cargo, vessels with but

two masts and a small spread of sail, these early
voyagers to our shores were the original founders
of our seafaring history. Braving storms at sea
and the dangers of a rocky, uncharted coast,
constantly on their guard against hostile Indians,
these first fishermen and traders dried their fish
on outlying islands and in secluded coves and
carried them to the West Indies and even to
Spain, Portugal, England, and France. So well
known, indeed, were these New England fishing

fleets and fishing stations that in May, 1622, after a winter of hunger for the Pilgrims, a settler at Plymouth — Edward Winslow by name — sailed northward in order to beg for food from the fishermen there for his famishing neighbors on Cape Cod.

Captain John Smith was one of these early navigators to our northern shores. Boys and girls of today are more likely to picture him in the Jamestown colony at Virginia and with Pocahontas, the Indian girl who saved his life when her father, the chief Powhatan, had taken him captive. But in 1614 he left Jamestown to become the first Englishman to sail along the Atlantic coast and to give New England, Massachusetts, and even Plymouth their very names. He was an explorer, a historian, and a mapmaker as well as a navigator and a trader. Like my grandfather, he went to sea at sixteen; and our early seafaring history owes everything to his daring and enterprise. On the rocky shores of Monhegan Island, off the Maine coast, he dried tons of codfish and sent one shipload to England and another to

Spain. He was, in fact, in a very real sense the forerunner and the founder of our foreign trade.

The master of the *Eliza Ann Chase* knew, too, about other dangerous voyages undertaken by other early ships, these built and manned in American seaport towns. Following upon the trading in fish, or side by side with it, came the carrying from New England to Old England of great masts and timbers for the ships of the Royal British Navy of King Charles II. Pine, spruce, and oak trees, some of them three feet thick at the base and one hundred feet in height, were cut down in the virgin forests of Maine and New Hampshire. These were dragged by many yoke of oxen to the nearest harbors and there loaded upon the waiting vessels. As early as the year 1666 a famous diarist of England, Samuel Pepys, wrote: "There is also the very good news of 4 New England ships come safe to Falmouth with masts for the King." And as the cargoes increased in variety and weight, so our ships were built longer and larger, able to carry more sail and to bear more tons in their holds and on their decks.

Among the many voyages of our eighteenth and early nineteenth century ships none were more exciting and fraught with peril than those undertaken to the northwest shores of America in search of furs from the Indians there. These long and dangerous voyages, begun shortly after the Revolutionary War had come to an end in 1783, lasted for some twenty-five years. Although the ships of Boston and Salem had been foremost in this Northwest fur trade, those from Maine, then a

part of Massachusetts, had not been lacking. More than one Blue Hill captain had risked his life and the lives of his crew in this profitable, if perilous enterprise. Young Captain Chase's own grandfather had been among their reckless number; and as a boy he had heard all manner of hair-raising tales about that faraway northwestern coast and its great river, the Columbia.

This early traffic in furs had arisen as a means of trade with China, a trade in which American ships were in competition with those of other nations, particularly with the British. What American ship merchants and shipmasters were searching after, in those years when the end of war had brought a new opportunity for safe trading by sea, was some commodity which would appeal to the wealthy classes in China and the sale of which would yield a substantial, if not, indeed, a fabulous profit. This commodity they found in the skins of fur-bearing animals, the seal, the beaver, and especially in the black, shining pelts of the sea otter. And since such furs were most plentiful in the forests and along the shores of Vancouver Island, this dangerous, lonely coast-line became the goal of our ships and sailors.

Men and boys who embarked upon such a voyage as this (and there were boys of fourteen and even of twelve who did so) knew that they might well be away from home for two or even for three years. They must have known, too, the dangers which they faced. The ships which they manned as masters and officers or as ordinary sea-men and cabin boys were laden with all manner of goods for barter with the Indians, whose reputation for savagery was well known. These goods included rolls of bright cotton cloth, beads, nails, a variety of tools, axes, gimlets, saws, and chisels, jew's-harps and other simple musical instruments, sheets of bright copper, pocket mirrors, cheap rings and bracelets, hundreds of pairs of shoes, blankets in vivid colors, tin kettles — in short every type of gadget, trinket, or toy which might appeal to the natives of those faraway coasts.

The dangers of such a voyage began with the voyage itself. First, Cape Horn with its contrary winds and enormous seas must be weathered and rounded; and this stormy passage was one of the most difficult of all seafaring routes. Once its black, tossing waters had been conquered, the ships sailed northward toward their destination, usually stopping at some islands, at the Marquesas, where they could procure bananas, breadfruit, and coconuts for sailors hungry for fruit, or at Galápagos, where they might find a giant tortoise which would yield fresh and quite delicious meat.

When finally they had cast their anchors in
Nootka Sound, the fur-trading center of Vancouver, dangers multiplied, for the Chinook Indians
were a fierce and dangerous lot, who resented

invaders to their shores even while they longed
for the strange wares brought in the invading
ships. Tiah Chase as a boy was familiar with the
long scar on his grandfather's cheek, given him

by an Indian tomahawk before he had hurled
the Chinook from his quarterdeck. He was familiar, also, with the tales of slaughtered seamen
who had ventured too far ashore in their boats
and become the prey of deadly Chinook arrows.
The Indians, however, as the fur trade grew, became terrified in their turn by the cannon and
swivel-guns, muskets, pistols, and cutlasses which
the fur-trading ships depended on more and
more for protection against savage raids. And
after all, what was danger, Tiah's grandfather had
said, when two hundred otter skins, worth fifty
dollars each in China, could be purchased from
these devils for two hundred cheap chisels or an
equal number of small pocket mirrors? For otter
skins were of little value to the savages compared
to these wonderful products of a distant civili-
zation.

Often the ships lingered for as much as a year
off Vancouver, waiting to receive all the available furs from that region and even from the
forests farther north. Sometimes during those
waiting months their captains sailed them south-

ward along the coast of California to do a bit of trading there also. They sailed them into the beautiful harbor of Monterey, then the old Spanish capital, and to Santa Barbara and San Diego, where they met the early Franciscan *padres* at their Missions.

Returning northward once more to a far bleaker coast, they finally set forth, once their ships were laden with their precious freight, upon their long three months' voyage across the Pacific. Almost invariably, after three or four weeks of sailing, they put in at Hawaii, not only to obtain more fresh foods in the shape of Hawaiian pineapples and the fat meat of island hogs, but also to pick up logs of fragrant sandalwood, which, they had discovered with their Yankee shrewdness, would also sell at a tremendous profit in Canton.

Cabin boys who started their seafaring life on ships in the Northwest fur trade were often tall young men before they saw again the shores of their New England towns, for such a voyage took them truly around the world. Once their ships had reached Canton on its great ship-laden river and had sold their thousands of sea-otter skins, their beaver, seal, and sandalwood, the generous sums gained from such sales were invested in tea, Chinese porcelain, beautiful oriental silks, and shawls. Then the heavily laden vessels hoisted their sails and embarked upon their homeward way, a voyage of several months at best, down the China Sea, through the dangerous straits and among the many islands of the Indian Ocean, westward toward the Cape of Good Hope, which was the turning point on their long course toward New York or Boston.

The Indian Ocean held its dangers, too, not alone from submerged rocks, treacherous currents, and tricky winds, but from South Sea pirates, who were more ferocious than the Chinook Indians. These bands of ruthless criminals lay in wait to swarm upon any ship that missed her course and ran aground on some low-lying coral reef. In many an old New England graveyard there still stand today stones whose brief terse words only suggest the many perils risked by fur traders to the Northwest and to China:

Sacred to the memory of two youths, William Peters, aged 16, and his brother George, aged 18, killed by pirates off Java Head in the year 1796.

This stone records the death of John Sturgis, aged 17, at the hands of Indians on Vancouver Island in the year 1801.

These events of the past, thrilling as they were to the captain of the *Eliza Ann Chase,* were of far less importance than the exciting happenings of his own day which were taking place before his very eyes. In every foreign harbor he entered, he saw the towering masts and spars of the ships of many nations; and of them all, so he thought (and not without truth), none were so splendid as those of his own country. On every ocean, too, he hailed them, their great sails firmly set, their high, or bluff, or long, sleek bows cutting the waves, their holds laden with every product the wide world offered to its people of every continent.

Sometimes he and his family saw from his quarterdeck a great burst of white sail cutting the horizon, perhaps on the Atlantic working southward toward Cape Horn on the long way toward the Far East, perhaps on the Indian Ocean leaving Java on a westbound course around Good Hope. Soon the white sails, drawing nearer before the wind, revealed the bluff bows and square stern of a Boston East Indiaman, one of the fastest ocean ships of her time and descendant of some fifty years of far-flung maritime enterprise and experience.

Perhaps no other ship was so stately as an East Indiaman, which had been built in the great shipyards of the Kennebec River in Maine or of the Merrimack in Massachusetts and designed for trade with Far Eastern ports. Painted black in contrast to her taut white sails, which hung not only from her main masts and spars, but from every possible place in her lofty rigging, she was a thrilling sight to see, resembling, my grandmother used to say, some vast family washing hung out to dry in the wind.

She might be on her way to Calcutta or Batavia or Singapore, laden with boots and shoes, sewing machines, clocks and watches, needles and thread, chairs, tables, desks, plows, printing presses, picks,

shovels, grindstones, rum, organs, canned sea-
foods, and a hundred other Yankee products, unknown yet desirable to the brown-skinned people
of India and the South Seas. Or she might be
returning home to bring the rich smell of coffee,
ginger, cloves, tea, and pepper into the gray,
cold waters of Cape Cod or to the noisy wharves
of New York's waterfront.

She might instead be carrying in her deep hold
quite a different cargo toward the tropics and
seemingly a strange one, a cargo conceived in
the imaginative and ambitious mind of a young
man named Frederic Tudor. While he was still
hardly out of his teens, this farseeing boy was
beset by the idea that ice might be successfully
shipped to the hot countries and islands of the
earth. Nature had already paid the cost of it, he
thought, so that, if only some means could be
discovered to keep it from melting on its long
journeys, vast profits might be won from its sale.
To discover this means of insulation from heat
became Frederic Tudor's passion. For years he
experimented with all manner of means, with rice,

hay, chaff, shavings, cheerfully enduring the laughter and scorn of his friends and neighbors who thought him completely mad. Finally he found his answer in sawdust, and thereupon began to ship his cold cargo, cut from a hundred New England ponds and lakes, first to the West Indies and then to India and the South Sea islands. Indian princes and rajahs, merchants and thirsty islanders learned from him to relish cold drinks and in their sweltering climes blessed the name of Tudor. And so successful did his extraordinary venture prove that it made his name renowned throughout the seafaring world and won him the title of the "Ice King."

Often a quite different sort of ship was overhauled and hailed, a slow ship with burly bows and heavy stern, her patched sails blackened by smoke and grease, her broad, deep hull laden with barrels of oil. She was a whaler. Her home port was New Bedford, or New London, or Nantucket. She roamed the seas from the Arctic to the South Pacific in search of those monsters of the deep which must surface now and again to send great jets of foam high into the air. When one of them had been harpooned by her daring seamen in their rowboats, it was hauled alongside the whaler and its mighty carcass hacked into generous slabs of blubber, which were then boiled down on her decks to extract its precious oil. Some whales yielded up their bone as well and sperm whales their wax. The lights in millions of American homes and on thousands of American streets were assured by this hazardous enterprise — not to mention the slender waists of ladies in America and elsewhere who used the whalebone for the "stays" in their corsets!

But of all the ships young Captain Chase was destined to sight during those eleven years of sailing, none afforded such excitement and admiration as did the clippers, those triumphs of American building and of American mastery over the seas. These ocean greyhounds had but a brief life of some ten years; yet they made those ten years the proudest, most glorious decade of our seafaring history.

Clipper ships were built with one consuming

purpose, that of *speed*. Although they were larger and longer than the older sailing vessels, most of them being two hundred feet or more in length and able to carry one thousand to two thousand tons of cargo, it was not their size which made them what they were, but rather the character of their shape and rigging. They were graceful, lithe ships, lower and sharper at both bow and stern than the earlier models, narrower in breadth in proportion to their greater length, and able to carry a vast expanse of sail from their loftier masts and spars and their much longer yards. Even the sails crowded on an East Indiaman were as nothing to those carried by the swiftest clipper ships. Indeed, the canvas which a clipper could spread when she was running before a fair wind was actually five times what the stoutest East Indiaman dared to carry. Such a ship, as she tore past the *Eliza Ann Chase* with her sails fully set, must have reminded my grandmother of the mightiest of Monday washings!

Speed was the watchword and the goal of all the clippers, as their very name suggests; and in the year 1850, when some of the most famous of them were built and launched, speed meant speed to one place, the coast of California and the frenzied port of San Francisco, which had grown almost over night from a small trading post and Mission station to a great city. The gold-seekers, the Forty-niners, were hurrying there, and they must be housed, clothed, and fed.

Only a few of the men feverish for gold traveled by clippers. Even though the great ships had had room for them, the fares were much too high for average men. Instead many chartered older, smaller vessels for the journey round Cape Horn; or more sailed to the Isthmus of Panama which they crossed in mule wagons, and then boarded other vessels waiting for them on the Pacific side; or some, of course, took the long trek across the country in their covered wagons.

It was the business of the clippers and their daring, resolute captains to carry tons of cargo: chairs and tables and beds, hewn lumber, window sashes, panes of glass and even complete house frames, picks and shovels, boots and shoes, cloth-

ing of every description, kitchen utensils, and countless tons of food. They had been designed for such a purpose by their master builders, men such as Samuel Hall of Boston and Donald Mc-Kay, born in Nova Scotia; and they clipped southward around the Horn and up the Pacific, battling tremendous seas and winds that tore at their rigging, at a speed which astonished the world. In 1851 the *Flying Cloud*, a masterpiece of McKay genius, made a record voyage, covering sea miles which once had taken four months and more, in just eighty-nine days from New York to San Francisco. And once she and her rivals had made San Francisco, they either raced back homeward for more supplies or else sped across the Pacific to Canton, or Hongkong, or Shanghai to load with tea, not alone for American markets, but for British ports as well. Or some of them might spread their wide white wings for Australia, where Englishmen were migrating in thousands and where gold had been discovered also, carrying the same necessities for life in a new land and bringing back wool, grain, and hides.

These insolent, defiant, saucy clipper ships caught the imagination of the seafaring world one hundred years ago. No other country could match these splendid creations of American minds and American dreams. They marked a revolution in naval architecture; and they were the wonder of their day. They made records which even ocean steamships were not to defeat for fully twenty-five years, voyages never equaled by sailing ships before or since their brief era. Their very names suggested their power of swift flight through fair or stormy waters: the *Lightning*, the *Flying Fish*, the *Sea Witch*, the *Winged Racer*, the *Meteor*, the *Snow Squall*, the *Cyclone*, the *Shooting Star*, the *Herald of the Morning*, the *Sovereign of the Seas*.

These great ships were beautiful as well as swift and haughty. Their long hulls were painted black, their portholes and deck railings often outlined in white; their brass fittings were kept highly polished; their cabins, painted white on the outside, were sumptuous with costly woods, mahogany and rosewood. They carried extra spars to replace those that might be broken by destructive winds and fresh white canvas to replace torn or even dingy sails. When they cut the waters of a home or a foreign port, with their towering white sails, their freshly painted high white spars, their pine decks holystoned to a smooth cream color, their brilliant company flags flying from their lofty main-trucks, the Stars and Stripes billowing from their sterns, they were truly a majestic sight, at which all on the waterfronts stared in admiration and astonishment.

The commanders of such marvels were men of the finest sort, courageous, adventuresome, and yet careful. They drove their ships by every possible adaptation to wind, sea, and weather; yet they knew that the slightest miscalculation or the least error in judgment might mean not only loss of time, but even disaster. Most of them had shipped at fourteen or sixteen, or even at twelve years as cabin boys on lesser craft and had steadily worked their way up to the proudest position the sea could offer. Some were young men still in their twenties or early thirties; others were older and long used to sailing and its ways. Their names and their ships became known around the world: Captain Philip Dumaresq, a Maine man, and his ship, the *Surprise;* Captain Josiah Cressey, of Marblehead and the famous *Flying Cloud;* Captain Joshua Patten, commander of the *Neptune's Car,* and his extraordinary young wife, Mary Brown Patten, who herself for fifty-two anxious days commanded the great ship; Captain Robert Waterman, a cabin boy at the age of ten years, and his ship, the *Challenge,* upon which he once outwitted a mutinous and murderous crew of ruffians on a voyage around Cape Horn.

Many uncontrollable events caused the end of the Clipper Ship Era: the financial depression of the years 1857 to 1859; the facts that such great ships were costly to build and to operate and that the very power of their speed took its toll in wear and consequent depletion; the coming of the Civil War, which for four years put an end to much of our foreign commerce; the settlement of our western plains and prairies, which took men's minds from the sea; and, above all else, the steady substitution of steam for sail upon every ocean. Yet it was a triumphant and a glorious era. The memory of the great ships which it produced and of the brave men who commanded them will always stir our imaginations and arouse our pride in the seafaring history of our country.

The *Eliza Ann Chase* was neither a stately East Indiaman nor a record-breaking clipper; but she was a fine sturdy ship for all that. And because, in her size, her rigging and her tonnage she was far more typical of a thousand American merchant ships of her time than was either a clipper or an East Indiaman, it will perhaps be interesting to learn of her voyages and her cargoes during those eleven years between 1850 and 1861 when she was mastered by my grandfather and carried my grandmother as his constant companion.

Captain Melatiah Chase was, like many other

shipmasters of his day, in what may be called the "general trade." This term means that his ship was chartered by several firms of ship merchants, in Portland or Boston, New York or Baltimore, now one and now another, depending upon their need for a reliable, well-mastered ship and upon whether the *Eliza Ann Chase* were available at just the right time. Such practice on the part of a captain who owned as well as commanded his ship meant that the voyages which he took were as various as were the cargoes he carried. In common phrase, he was his own boss, could look with a careful eye upon companies of merchants, study the freight rates which would be paid him for his cargoes, and, to a large extent, make up his own mind as to where he could most profitably sail his ship. The logbooks of the *Eliza Ann Chase* during those eleven years show clearly that her captain was not given to any one route or voyage, but instead sailed her over all seas and into many harbors.

Sometimes she went on short voyages to the West Indies carrying lumber to Havana —

timbers, pine boards, or perhaps thousands of well-made packing boxes — and bringing home molasses and sugar. Sometimes she sailed with cotton goods, boots and shoes, and all manner of household furnishings to the beautiful harbor of Rio de Janeiro, lying below the towering Organ Mountains with their peaks six thousand feet in height, and brought home tons of fragrant coffee;

or to Buenos Aires after hides and sheepskins; or to Valparaiso on the coast of Chile after copper and other mineral products. She made several voyages to the Mediterranean with a mixed cargo from New England mills and factories and sailed homeward laden with oranges and lemons, currants and raisins, olive oil, and great casks of wine. My grandmother, when I was a little girl, used to tell us how she loved these Mediterranean voyages. For on at least two occasions she was left with her little girls at the home of some American merchants in the white, ancient city of Cádiz in Spain, a welcome change from the sea, while the captain of the *Eliza Ann Chase* sailed her eastward to Smyrna. There the ship loaded with the best figs in the world and brought them back to Boston, together with Cádiz wine and salt. She sailed also, as did the clippers, to California, making as safe a voyage around the Horn as they, even though she could not compete with their speed; and then, like them, crossed the Pacific to China after tea, weathering the difficult passages among the islands of the Indian Ocean toward the Cape of Good Hope and home.

Thus the ports and harbors of a dozen strange countries became less strange to my grandmother and her daughters — as to many other women and children — than their own quiet New England bays and coves when they returned to them after months and even years at sea. How I used to envy them when I was young and wish that I might have seen a sampan off the China coast or an albatross off Cape Horn, or heard a Spanish cavalier, with a plume in his hat and a red sash around his waist, strumming his guitar and singing a song in the moonlight of old Cádiz!

3

"Danger always trails a deep-water sailor," an old sea captain of my childhood used to say. It was true enough. One danger after another shadowed the sailor. It might be danger from pirates in the South Seas, or from icebergs in northern waters; or danger from a fall from lofty yards on a pitching, rolling ship; or danger from a sudden surge of water tearing across a careening deck; or danger from mutiny, or from fire, or from running upon hidden rocks and reefs. But of all dangers none was so ever-present as danger from those great natural forces, the winds — sometimes fair and kind, to be sure, but more often tempestuous and perilous.

There was something ironic and even cruel about this danger from the winds, for they, with all their terrors, were the chief friends and allies of the sailing ships. Without them there could have been no sailing ships. Winds alone gave the ships their lives, their passages around the world; and yet these very winds in their mighty force could give also destruction and death.

Winds were mysterious and awful powers to the earliest sailors, who, thousands of years ago off the coasts of Egypt and Phoenicia, Greece and Rome, and countless islands of the Mediterranean and Aegean Seas, began to hoist great pieces of sewn leather or of stout cloth on their rude masts in order to help men toiling at long oars in rough seas. All they knew about the winds came from experience and observation as they began to venture ever farther out to sea. For the science of the winds is a very difficult one; and little was known about it by the average navigator of any age until fairly recent days.

At just about the time when Captain Melatiah

Chase entered upon his eleven years of commanding his own ship, a young Virginian named Matthew Fontaine Maury, who had been a midshipman in the United States Navy until he had to leave his post because of an injury, designed and published for the use of ships his famous *Wind and Current Charts*. These charts were

WINDS AND BEST SAILING ROUTES
FOR THE MONTH OF JULY.

ROUTES ⟶ ⟶ ⟶ ⟶

PREVAILING WINDS ⟹

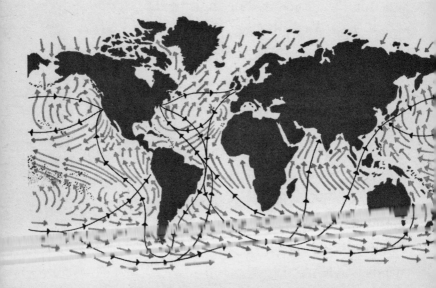

the result not only of observation at sea and of studying the logbooks of many vessels, but of a knowledge of physics and mathematics as well. They proved beyond a doubt that the winds, which heretofore to most sailors had seemed mysterious and even capricious forces, were governed by natural laws and by theories possible of discovery. His charts became before many years such a boon to ships and their navigators both in the saving of time and in the averting of danger that the man who designed them was known as the "Pathfinder of the Seas."

While Tiah Chase was still a cabin boy (before Lieutenant Maury had through his charts banished superstition and quieted many fears), he learned that the most important knowledge in a sailor's life was a practical knowledge of the winds, their natures, the directions from which they blew, what the term "prevailing winds" meant, when to trust them and when to watch them at every moment, ready at an instant's notice to do battle with them and with their sudden, unpredictable shiftings and gusts. He learned early the differing characters of these currents of the air upon which his life depended, as did the lives of all men who sailed the seas. He learned, too, that the routes of ships — the directions in which they sailed from one continent to another — were governed largely by these great planetary winds. And of all the winds that blew from the four corners of the heavens, he knew before his first voyage was over that those upon which a ship depended most were the "Roaring Westerlies" and the "Trades."

The roaring westerlies were the winds most dreaded by sailors. They were, to be sure, indispensable to a ship's swift passage; yet they were treacherous and cruel winds, responsible for the loss of many a ship, as they had been responsible for the wrecking of the *Sarah E. Snow*, described in the first chapter. They were the prevailing winds which blew across the two hemispheres, circling the earth in the temperate zones of both north and south. When a ship left the eastern shores of North America, perhaps from the port of Boston or of New York, bound for Liverpool or for London, she was at the mercy of these winds. It was they that made possible a swift, though usually stormy passage for her as she ran before them with her sails carefully set against their fury. Again, when a ship had rounded the Cape of Good Hope, bound eastward on her long five-thousand-mile run to Australia, she was in the path of the southern westerlies, which would drive her onward toward her goal. Both the northern and the southern westerlies were tempestuous winds which blew up mountainous seas to crash over the decks and demanded constant watching. One sail too many, and the best of ships might founder, to find herself on her beam ends, her masts and spars no longer upright but lying helplessly above the raging ocean. The roaring westerlies off Cape Horn or Good Hope or in the North Atlantic or Pacific could tell many a mocking tale of their tragic triumph over the most skillful of navigators.

No contrast could be more marked than the passage out of the cold zones of the westerlies into the mild, fair regions of the trade winds. These steady, benign, genial trades which blew toward the Equator, whether north or south, and which southbound ships picked up somewhere in the neighborhood of the Azores, the Madeiras, or the Hawaiian Islands, were the winds beloved of all sailors. Beneath them, the blue sea rolled gently on; above them, skies were clear or touched with light fleecy clouds; before them, a ship could safely spread all her canvas and speed on for days without so much as trimming a single sail. In such quiet safe waters dolphins and flying fish played around the ship. Seamen now had time to lounge about the decks, splicing ropes, smoking their pipes, singing, whittling, exchanging yarns, enjoying to the full this life they had embarked upon. Officers had no need in the trade winds to watch every rope, line, and spar, every inch of sail, every cloud in the sky. Children on board could play safely on dry and steady decks. Shipmasters could pace their quarters, or bend over their logs and charts, or sleep long nights in their cabins without an anxiety in the world.

Lesser winds than the westerlies held their dangers also. The monsoons, blowing off China and over the Indian Ocean, often brought sudden gusts and squalls with thunder, lightning, and torrential rains. A typhoon in the western Pacific in the neighborhood of Japan, or China, or the Philippine Islands was a violent, whirling, circular wind which all sailors feared. Hurricanes in West Indian waters or off Cape Hatteras, like the one which had dealt destruction to *The Bride*, were always capable of dealing out trouble or even ruin.

There was danger of quite another sort from the absence of any wind at all. When a ship struck a dead calm in the Indian Ocean or in the Doldrums, that wide, breathless stretch of sea between the equatorial coasts of South America and Africa, she might loiter there for weeks on end, her great sails hanging listlessly from the yards, waiting in vain to catch the most fitful and fleeting breeze. There were other terrors then

on that motionless, glassy sea beneath the continual glare of the blazing sun — terrors of heat, of thirst, and of failing provisions to feed a hungry crew, terrors of delay which might spell financial risk or total loss. And as the endless days dragged on, there came an almost ghostly fear that a wind would never come to rescue them from a stillness more foreboding of disaster than any peril the roaring westerlies at their worst could produce from their black heavens and from their monstrous seas.

Although my grandmother sailed for those eleven years in comparative safety after her honeymoon voyage, she never in her later life forgot the winds and their awful terrors. When I was a little girl and a strong northeast gale with snow and sleet smote our safe harbor, she always thought of the ships at sea, fewer now than in her sailing days yet still plying their ways in spite of the steamships that had begun to rule the ocean.

"Pray for all sailors tonight," she would say to us at bedtime. "Don't forget while you are safe and warm to pray for all the ships far out at sea."

4

SEAFARING EVEN at its best was a rugged and a dangerous way of life, one hardly suited to women and children. Yet there were many women of my grandmother's day who, married to sea captains, preferred its roughness and its perils to waiting at home for their husbands' returns or to bringing up their children singlehanded. They doubtless had their fears; but even fears in companionship were preferable to loneliness, uncertainty, and dread.

Before the year 1840 there are few recorded instances of seafaring wives. There was, however, at least one honeymoon voyage as early as 1795. At that time an eighteen-year-old shipmaster named James Howland of New Bedford, Massachusetts, took his still younger bride with him to the ports of the Baltic Sea. Just how these two young people made out on their romantic adventure we do not know; but at all events they returned home in safety, and probably Mrs. Howland was the center of conversation in her native town for months on end.

Throughout the twenty years between 1840 and 1860, years we have already seen as a banner period in American seafaring, the custom of women accompanying their husbands became common; and in the years following the Civil War — the last decades of the sailing ships — it had even become a general practice, particularly in New England families. In a letter written from Bordeaux in 1844, a Massachusetts captain says that out of nine American ships at anchor in that French harbor five of the masters have their wives with them and all are enjoying the presence of these ladies at dinners and gay parties on board one vessel or another. In another letter, this one written by my grandmother in 1857 from London to her parents in Maine, she describes vividly how seven New England wives from ships at anchor in London Pool waited together for two hours in front of Buckingham Palace to see Queen Victoria drive through its great gates in her open carriage behind her splendid horses.

When I was a child at the turn of the present century, I knew at least a dozen women in the small village of Blue Hill who, like my grandmother, had all gone to sea on board their husbands' ships; and several of these, like her, had taken their children with them. As I listened to their stories of foreign cities, heard their tales of this and that stirring incident, and was allowed to play with the treasures they had brought back home with them, strange shells, coral and amber necklaces, ivory elephants, pieces of Chinese jade, and tiny inlaid boxes, I felt deprived and even resentful that I had been born too late to share in the pleasures as well as the perils of such a life.

For there were pleasures as well as perils in a life at sea. My grandmother used to tell us of the

long, safe, quiet days when the *Eliza Ann Chase* ran before the trade winds, of walks on the decks under the warm blue skies, of hours spent in reading or in sewing on the quarterdeck, always reserved for the captain and his wife. Women at sea had no household duties. The cooking was done by the ship's cook in his galley, the waiting and tending by the ship's steward, the cleaning by seamen, small odd jobs by the cabin boys. The captain's wife, as the only woman allowed at sea, was a lady on board ship and had no menial work to do except in case of sickness or of an unforeseen emergency. She was respected by the officers and highly regarded by all the common seamen, even though these called her among themselves the "Old Woman," regardless of her age, just as they called their captain and commander the "Old Man."

Sewing was a major pursuit among all captains' wives. Sitting on the quarterdeck in fair weather or beneath the cabin skylight on days of wind, fog, or storm, these seagoing women fashioned all manner of needlework and embroidery, often in careful and intricate designs: napkins and tablecloths, towels and bedspreads, handkerchiefs, bags and purses, and every conceivable piece of underwear. My grandmother, before she had baby clothes to think of, always made her husband's shirts of fine linen with tucked fronts, which he would wear at dinner on some ship in a foreign port toward which they were sailing or at some party given by an American ship merchant living abroad. One old woman whom I knew when I was young was much given to deploring the loss of a vast amount of such handiwork when her husband's ship was wrecked off Java Head. "Just think," she used to say. "Forty-eight embroidered table napkins, fifteen crocheted tea towels, a tablecloth of drawn lace, and ten pairs of ruffled drawers, all thrown to the sharks!" She seemed to think these triumphs a great loss, forgetting that she had saved something far more priceless, merely her life itself!

Some shipmasters, too, were not above employing their hands in like manner during hours of freedom. Although their work was less fine than that of their wives, they hooked or braided rugs, wove cloth at looms, or worked at tapestries to cover chairs or stools. Several even became amateur painters of marine scenes or of ships; and many made ship models.

There were sudden and exciting things to see, especially in fair weather. Gulls often followed the ships, and, although they were many miles from land, they yet gave welcome assurance that there *was* land where they had their nests. Sometimes even familiar land birds during the migratory seasons would flutter above and about the decks in search of food. There were porpoises to watch, wheeling and circling in perfect rhythm through wave after wave, down and up again, in and out, as though they played a merry game known only to themselves; or a whale rolling his mammoth body like the hull of some derelict vessel, his great spout rising high into the air. Always there were changes in the sky and the clouds, and, after a shower, a rainbow arching the whole wide heavens and sending its shimmer-

ing colors deep down into the water. The stars
and the planets at night blazed with a fire unknown to stars over the land: Orion pursuing his
hunt across the sky; red Aldebaran; Arcturus, sure
and still; brilliant Sirius; and in tropical waters
the wonder of the Southern Cross.

The most anxious hours for any woman at sea
were the long hours of those days when the arrival
of a baby was close at hand. Shipmasters so soon
to become fathers fervently hoped, of course, to
make a port in time for this great event; yet wind
and weather sometimes made this hope impos-
sible of fulfillment. By tradition perhaps more
than by any actual training, the chief officer (the
first mate) was supposed to stand by in such an
emergency, just as he bore the main responsibility

for the treatment of illness among the crew. All ships carried a book of medical advice for those at sea, as well as a medicine chest of remedies, salves, ointments, calomel, castor oil, spirits of niter, iodine, and splints and bandages for broken bones; and this book contained specific instructions for the delivery of a baby. Yet a chief officer faced with such an emergency in a narrow cabin, with an agitated father trying helplessly to help him, and with a patient to encourage and care for — more terrified than she had ever been of the most awful perils of wind and waves — was hardly a man to be envied! Still, babies *were* born at sea, in storms and calms, off Cape Horn and in the tropics; and most of them lived to tell their children and grandchildren of their odd and exciting entrance into this world.

In the Maine village of Searsport, a place widely known for its ships and sailors, there is a list said to be "incomplete" of seventy-five children born at sea to Searsport parents during the last half of the nineteenth century. Of the seventy-five, only one failed to yell lustily when the relieved chief officer slapped his back.

Women at sea met other anxieties and terrors also with a resourcefulness and gallantry hardly conceivable today. Not a few of them had the intelligence and foresight to learn all they could about the ways of a ship, never knowing when they might be called upon to use such knowledge. They grew expert at studying winds and currents, learning to untangle the intricacy of rigging, the trimming of sails. Some under the tutelage of their husbands grew familiar with ships' charts, the points of their courses, even with the mathematics and the art of navigation. One remarkable example of almost incredible courage and discipline on the part of a woman is still recalled with pride and wonder by all who love the sea and know something of life under sail one hundred years ago.

This woman — or girl, for she was but nineteen years old — was Mary Brown of Boston, who appeared briefly in the second chapter. She had been married at sixteen to Captain Joshua Patten, a Maine man, who had followed the sea from his boyhood and was at thirty-five in the year 1856 commander of the clipper ship *Neptune's Car*. In June of that year the *Neptune's Car* sailed from New York, bound around Cape Horn for San Francisco. The weather off the Cape was particularly cold and stormy, for of course it was winter south of the Equator. Captain Patten from exposure, anxiety, and overwork became stricken with brainfever, which shortly caused him to become completely blind. The situation on board the great clipper was made even more perilous by the behavior of the chief officer, who had already been put in irons for insubordination and neglect of duty. The second mate was a loyal and able officer, but he was ignorant of navigation.

Young Mary Brown Patten immediately took

over the complete command of the ship, grateful beyond words that she had acquired the necessary knowledge upon her honeymoon voyage around the globe three years before. For fifty-two days this girl, together with caring for her husband, navigated a great ship, heavily rigged and of eighteen hundred tons' burden, through wind and storm, gave her commands to the lesser officers — for she refused to allow the now penitent chief officer to return to duty — and brought the *Neptune's Car* safely into the harbor of San Francisco.

We are used to the saying that "the sea made men." Clearly, it could make women as well!

5

My grandparents always felt sorry that they had no son to take to sea with them on the *Eliza Ann Chase*. Their one son, my father, was born just at the time when they left the sea, at the beginning of the Civil War in 1861; and their two daughters, Ann and Abby, who did go with them as little children, were almost too young to gain all that such an experience had to offer them. There were many American boys and girls, however, who in the 1850's and in the years following the Civil War were of precisely the right age, not only to enjoy vastly a life at sea, but to learn a hundred unfamiliar things both from its daily

routine and from the foreign harbors into which they sailed. This right age lay roughly between ten and fourteen years. Before they were ten, they were too young to savor thoroughly their unique life; by the time they were thirteen or fourteen and ready for an academy or high school, their parents were likely to leave them at home for studies usually not available on board a ship.

For these lucky boys and girls of a hundred years ago, the unparalleled adventure of a long

foreign voyage always began with the bustle and confusion of getting under way. Let us imagine ourselves with them at a Boston or New York wharf and see precisely what they would have seen.

Standing with their parents on the quarterdeck, they watch the thick brown ropes cast off from the wharf posts, the sailors running around the capstan to bring up the anchor and singing some song, which in an odd way helps them to work in unison through their common, raucous stresses on its words:

> *The ship went sailing out over the bar,*
> > *O Rio! O Rio!*
> *Turn away, love, away,*
> > *Away down Rio.*

Other men and boys spring into the rigging, scurrying aloft up the ratlines like agile monkeys, sprawling on the great, horizontal yards to set free the white widths of sail which will soon catch the first breath of the wind outside the harbor mouth. These are singing, too, their words floating downward as they secure or loosen what seem to be a thousand baffling lines:

> *We're outward bound this very day,*
> > *Goodbye, fare you well!*
> > *Goodbye, fare you well!*

The children see at once that the busiest man on board at this time of getting under way is the first mate, or chief officer. The captain, in contrast, seems only to be watching all things from his station on the quarterdeck as he talks with the harbor pilot, who will sail with them as far as open water. It is the first mate who moves constantly across the deck boards from forecastle to cabin, his eyes everywhere at once, his mind only on the seamen, who spring to obey his curt commands. Although he is assisted by the second and third mates and the boatswain (the bo'sun in sea language) who from their positions on the deck pass on his orders, this anxious hour is his responsibility and his alone. He knows that his success in handling his crew is not only being carefully sized up by his captain, but gauged shrewdly by the crew themselves, most of whom he has never seen before. He must prove himself both stern and just, firm yet reasonable, call his orders quickly and sharply, with a curse now and then if some seaman takes his time to obey them. Respect for him must be won at once; each of his commands must be executed with alacrity and good humor; or his control over his men is already lost. For ruthless discipline begins in this decisive early hour; and he is the first to impose it.

Now the pilot has dropped over the side. His boat is bearing him ashore. The ship is already on her own, her sails taut before the wind. The countless masts and spars crowding the waterfront become each minute less distinct. All land sounds have faded away. The water, so lately soiled with drifting harbor rubbish, now is deep and clear, curling backward from the sharp bow

to rush aft in long swells and join the tumbling white wake beyond the stern.

The first mate, less on edge now that all things are going as they should, calls a last terse order to a surly-looking sailor in a greasy red stocking cap.

"Here, you landlubber in the red hat, lay aft and clear the ensign halyards! Make it lively now!"

With a prompt "Aye, aye, sir," the sailor obeys. Here, he has sensibly concluded, is a first mate who means to take no nonsense from anyone.

The freed Stars and Stripes billow from the stern; the helmsman bears down on the wheel to shape the course; the filled sails strain at their ropes. Soon the port and starboard watches will be chosen, and the men in each assigned their posts and duties.

"And you young landlubbers," says the now cheery first mate to the awed and excited new voyagers on the quarterdeck, "get below and stow away your dunnage. Eight bells will soon be striking, and that means time for dinner."

This same rigid discipline extended as well to all sailing youngsters, as they were quick to recognize. Rules on shipboard were to be instantly obeyed by the captain's children as well as by ordinary seamen, whether they were rules about one's possessions or rules about forbidden areas of the ship. In narrow, cramped quarters personal belongings, clothes or games, books or toys, had each its particular place, and there it was to be kept. Children were to stay strictly away from the cook's galley and from the forecastle (pronounced *fo'c'sle*) where the seamen lived. Nor could they go far forward for walks or for games unless they were attended by one of the mates, or by the bo'sun or the carpenter. Talk with sailors was forbidden. Even the cabin boy, who might be much the same age as the captain's son, was no companion on a ship. He was, instead, one of the crew; and although he might have been a playmate or even a relative at home, at sea he could claim none of these advantages or expect any special favors whatsoever. Many a cabin boy, indeed, exchanged not a word with the ship's captain, except in strict line of duty, from the beginning to the end of the longest voyage.

There were stern rules also, or at least an unalterable code of behavior, about illness or injury. Seasickness during the first few days of any voyage was to be expected and borne without undue complaint. If one fell on a careening or slippery deck, cries and tears were not anticipated, at least from a child of ten or older. He learned, with a stubborn pride to help him, to clench his teeth and take it, even when a cut must be sewn up by the somewhat rude surgery of the sailmaker, or a broken bone set in splints by the chief officer. A boy — or a girl for that matter — learned, too, before so much as a month aboard ship that there might well be more costly accidents and tragedies about which life at home had never taught them. A sailor aloft in a storm might fall into the sea, or, what was worse, upon the deck, if he lost his hold and tumbled downward in a sudden pitch of the ship; or tremendous seas which crashed without warning across the decks might take their toll of men. These were sad realities taught by a harsh, exacting life; and, although they might well be shocking and even terrifying to children, they had to be met and reckoned with.

There was yet another code of behavior about fear. For the sea held fears for the young as well as for those far older than they. Families at sea, boys and girls alike, did not scream or cry in high winds and cold, tossing seas. They learned, instead, to trust the captain, the officers, the seamen, and even the ship herself to weather the gales which would be sure to smite them before any voyage was over.

All these, together with the discipline which enforced them and the code which governed them, were difficult lessons, taught in a hard, relentless school; but boys and girls who learned them well were on the way to becoming men and women of tough fiber, ready to cope with any offerings of life.

What was the layout of such a floating home, its living quarters for the captain's family, for the officers, for the crew? Where did children eat, sleep, play, and keep their occasional pets?

The long deck of a merchant, that is, a cargo-bearing, ship was carefully divided by custom into space for officers and space for seamen. The quarterdeck, or the deck at the stern of the ship, was raised above the deck floor by a short flight of steps. This quarterdeck was the sacred province of the captain, or of the officers or mates, when they were called upon to assist him or to consult with him. Beyond the quarterdeck was the ship's wheel with its instruments of navigation; and forward of the wheel was the companionway, or flight of stairs, which led to the after, or main, cabin in which the captain's family lived. This cabin was lighted by square windows near its top, which was raised above the deck, and by a large skylight in the center. The captain's stateroom lay aft, off the main cabin, and there were as well adjoining this cabin smaller staterooms which were used by his family. Forward, across the narrow hall of the companionway, were the toilet facilities, perhaps even a bathroom, and the door, or doors, leading to the forward cabin itself. This cabin served as the dining room. It was long and narrow, since along its farther side were the staterooms for the officers and the steward.

Meals on a ship must have seemed curious at first to youngsters on board. The captain, his wife and family, and the chief officer were served earliest. They sat around the table in some state and were waited upon by the steward. After they had finished, the table was cleared and reset for the lesser officers. As for the common sailors, they had no table at all and many of them would have been amazed at one, and at knives and forks. Each had his own tin plate and his spoon, with which he ate his ladled-out food from a wooden mess tub brought steaming-hot from the galley to the deckhouse, usually by the cabin boy. The watches ate in turn, expecting nothing better than a thick stew with hunks of hardtack, or the almost constant fare of slabs of salted beef, which the men cut with their pocketknives and in derision called "salt horse," but which apparently had enormous staying powers for hard work. Sometimes on Sundays as a special treat they were given "plum duff," a mixture of flour and water boiled with raisins and sweetened with molasses.

Both after and forward cabins might well be pleasant rooms in fair weather when the sun shone through the windows and skylights, and when in the evening the children could read or play games in the lamplight. In the main cabin, or living room, there were easy chairs and tables, although while at sea these must be anchored securely to the floor. And, as in any living room on land, there were books and pictures, few in number, of course, but for that very reason more highly prized. No rooms on board ship were pleasant in very heavy weather, for water was bound to seep or even to pour into them; but that

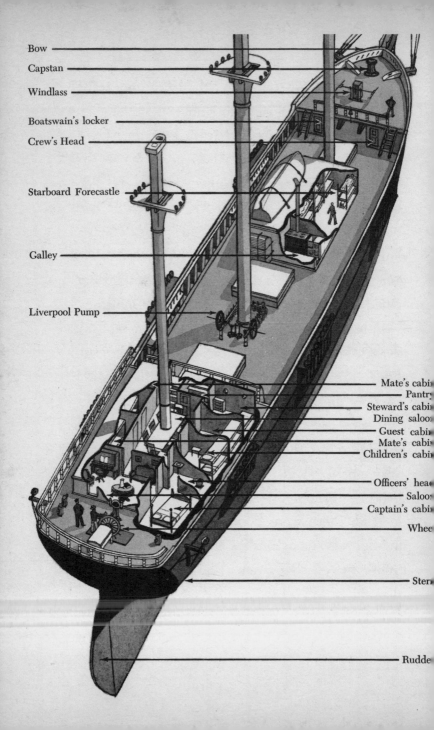

Bow

Capstan

Windlass

Boatswain's locker

Crew's Head

Starboard Forecastle

Galley

Liverpool Pump

Mate's cabin
Pantry
Steward's cabin
Dining saloon
Guest cabin
Mate's cabin
Children's cabin

Officers' head
Saloon
Captain's cabin

Wheel

Stern

Rudder

discomfort was just one of the many discomforts to be endured cheerfully at sea.

The seamen had their own cabin, their deckhouse or forecastle. This was well forward on the deck, between the foremast and the bow. It was likely to be a confusing room, littered with seamen's gear, with sea chests and dunnage bags, and often filled with wet clothing of every sort. Its walls were cut by bunks, one on top of another, where the sailors slept between the rough blankets which they had brought with them. The cook's galley was usually forward of the sailors' quarters, though often under the same roof; and under the same roof, too, was sometimes the small shop of the ship's carpenter. If animals were carried along for fresh meat, and these were usually hens or pigs, they were kept in pens built just forward of the deckhouse and near the galley.

Unlike hens and pigs, whose lives were, of course, doomed to start with, pets did not thrive at sea. Children who begged to be allowed to bring along their dogs or cats were almost certain of disappointment and even of grief. Dogs had no safe place to run. They missed woods and fields and the pleasures of sniffing at land smells. In high winds they were given to yelping and whining, both sounds hated and feared by the superstitious sailors. They clearly did not take to the sea, grew lifeless and homesick, and proved anything but good companions and faithful friends in the crowded cabins. As to cats, they rarely appreciated even the vast number of rats always present on a cargo ship and were of little practical use in their extermination. And if a kitten frolicked on deck in rough weather or a cat in a mad moment ran up a mast, mistaking it perhaps for a tree at home, they not infrequently met a sad and sudden fate.

The only pets which did seem to enjoy a sea voyage were the monkeys and the parrots which the seamen brought on board from some port in the Pacific or from the islands of the Indian Ocean. Children were forbidden any intimate association with these creatures, since the monkeys were filthy beasts who sheltered and enjoyed insect life of various sorts and since the profane and indecent words uttered by the parrots distressed all seagoing mothers. The sailors, however, delighted in their pets, regarding them as mascots and as purveyors of good luck and allowing them to mess up the forecastle as they liked. They carried the parrots on their shoulders and encouraged the monkeys to run up the rigging, hang aloft from their tails, or, squatting on some high perch, casually eat the vermin which infested them.

Fresh water was always a problem at sea, often necessitating an extra stop at ports or in some island harbor to replenish the supply. The iron water tank, which held from two to four thousand gallons, was sunk in the hold, beside the trunk of the great mainmast. When water was plentiful, buckets or kegs of it, known as scuttle butts, were filled daily for the use of all on board; when it was low, the second mate gave each seaman his allowance to drink at four o'clock in the afternoon just at the beginning of the short two-hour "dog watch." All depended, of course,

upon heavy rains to increase the supply, especially when any land at all was many miles away; and during such rains every keg and bucket was filled to the brim.

Children on board always welcomed with excitement the sudden violent showers of the tropics which often fell upon a calm, still sea. Then the seamen would close the scuppers in order to save the rain on the decks. Sometimes

it came in great warm sheets which covered the deck boards in a few minutes, real inches of water splashing and swirling about with the easy motion of the ship. Children then shed their clothes down to their shirts and underdrawers, washed themselves, and rolled about with shouts of laughter. On the forward deck sailors brought out their dirty dungarees, the cook the table linen and the galley cloths. There was great scrubbing with stiff brushes and strong soap. When the sun came out once more, the articles hanging in the lower rigging dried in its heat, and everyone felt a new cleanliness and respectability.

Food on board was usually plentiful, though it sometimes grew monotonous. The cook was often a Negro or sometimes a Chinese, since they had the reputation of being the best. The omnipresent salt beef and pork of the forecastle was not disdained by the captain's family, for a good cook could make it more than palatable in many ways. The hens and chickens on board varied the fare, and sometimes a porpoise was caught, whose steaks and liver were delicious. Butter was of the tinned variety, as were many of the fruits and vegetables. Condensed milk was necessarily used on most ships, although according to the records cows were occasionally carried. On the *Eliza Ann Chase* a goat was taken along on one voyage as being tidier than a cow, taking up less space, and giving richer milk. The goat, however, whose name was *Butter*, did not enjoy sea life and was wisely left in Barcelona to make Spanish friends.

And always in island harbors from the Azores to the Hawaiians there was vast excitement when small boats laden with fresh fruits came from the shore. These brought pineapples, oranges and lemons, coconuts, and great bunches of bananas, together with a variety of fresh meats, shellfish, and green, crisp vegetables. What a thrill it was to watch them approaching through the blue, still water and to know that at any moment during the afternoon one could strip a banana of its skin, see a swooping gull seize this instantly and watch greedily for yet another with its cold yellow eyes!

6

As I BEGIN to write this chapter about the many sorts and types of human beings who made up a ship's roll call from commander to cabin boy, I realize how very fortunate I am to have known personally and even intimately people who themselves spent many years at sea. Not only did I know, as a child and young girl, men who like my grandfather were shipmasters and women who like my grandmother accompanied their husbands, but I spent my early life among many others who as children had made voyages with their parents. Even when I entered college some fifty years ago, I knew as friends girls and boys there from Maine seafaring towns who had gone to sea in the 1880's and 1890's, in the final years of sailing ships. Two girls in my dormitory had been born on foreign voyages, one in Singapore, the other in the cabin of her father's ship off the coast of New Caledonia in the South Seas. Because of these lucky circumstances for me, I learned at first hand about many of the personalities I shall now describe without having to depend upon the excellent books written about them. For without any doubt one of the great advantages to be gained by those boys and girls who went to sea was an understanding of the various men who sailed with them and upon whom they depended for their well-being, their pleasure, and their safety.

We have already learned a good deal about the character of shipmasters who commanded their floating worlds, especially of those who sailed, as did Captain Melatiah Chase, during the great years of the American Merchant Marine between 1840 and 1860. It is hardly necessary to say that with so many men commanding so many ships there were some captains not of the high caliber of the best in their profession. This is, of course, true in all walks of life. Richard Henry Dana in his wonderful book *Two Years before the Mast*, in which he vividly relates his life as a common sailor on the ship *Pilgrim* before the year 1840, writes of his captain as a harsh, ruthless man for whom the seamen felt little but hatred, though this they had to conceal. Without doubt there were other such cruel and brutal captains; but they were clearly the exception. The typical commander of our best merchant ships was, as we have seen, a man of honor as well as of courage, who was justly proud of the position he had won through years of hard work. The responsibility for his ship's safe passage and for the safety of all on board was his moral obligation and his alone; and although in the very nature of things he must exact the utmost in manliness and loyalty from his officers and his seamen, in the great majority of cases he was himself an example to them of both. The stirring history of our merchant marine is filled with the resourcefulness, heroism, and wisdom of countless such shipmasters; indeed, to a large extent these men made its history and therefore deserve unstinted praise and admiration.

We have learned, also, not a little about the important status of the chief officer, or first mate. In most cases he, like his captain, had worked his way up from the forecastle and was himself in line for a command of his own. Through him the captain issued most of his orders; he had the care of allotting the tasks to the men on watch and of overseeing their performance; and he was largely responsible both for the behavior of the crew and for the spirit which bound them together to work as one man. He was expected, further-more, to be thoroughly familiar with navigation as well as with every minute detail of handling a great ship in any sort of weather.

Between him and the lesser mates, of which there were always two — the second and third, on a well-manned ship, and sometimes a fourth — there was a considerable gulf fixed. These lesser officers, although they ate in the forward

cabin at a second sitting and had rooms of their
own, were subordinate to the chief in every particular. They obeyed his orders unquestioningly,
attended to minor details about the decks, and
were not infrequently sent aloft like the seamen
to reef or furl the sails, or to free them. At the
same time they were expected to secure and to

hold the respect of the common sailors and to maintain the dignity of their rank.

Richard Henry Dana has a revealing story to tell about the second mate of the *Pilgrim,* an idle and worthless fellow from a well-to-do family, who had been sent off to sea by his father because he had failed to make use of a college education. This Mr. F—— was one night caught by the captain asleep at his watch. As watch officer he was responsible for the safety of the ship. The captain at once, in a tirade of just fury against such neglect of duty, called him a "lazy, good-for-nothing rascal, neither man, boy, nor sailor," banished him from the deck, and at dawn the next morning summoned all the seamen aft to tell them that F—— was no longer an officer. His duties as well as his title were conferred upon an intelligent young seaman named Jim Hall, who thereupon became *Mr.* Hall and whom the sailors were warned by the captain to obey as they would obey the captain himself. As for the wretched F——, he was consigned to the forecastle in well-merited disgrace.

One of these lesser officers, perhaps the third mate, might combine his duties with those of the bo'sun; or the job of bo'sun might be given to a lesser officer, who then had the title to himself. He was a sort of foreman over the seamen, whom he summoned to their watches by a sharp blast on his whistle (known as a bo'sun's pipe), always worn about his neck as the symbol of his office. He was the overseer, too, of the ship's lifeboats, which were carried both on top of the deck-houses or cabins and slung on davits at the ship's sides. The bo'sun had charge also of the care of the ship's anchor and of the condition of her rigging and sails. All this was most important work, demanding a thorough knowledge of ship machinery and gear; and the bo'sun was often a man of marked intelligence and training, for whom boys and girls on board held deep respect.

Two of the most interesting and indispensable men aboard ship were the carpenter and the sail-maker, known respectively as "Chips" and "Sails." Although neither had the status of an officer, they were in no sense common seamen but, rather,

masters of their trades. The carpenter in particular was often not a man hardened to the sea.
He went on a voyage now and then as occasion
offered or inclination moved him. His work on
board was to rebuild or repair anything from
cabin furnishings to deck bulwarks and railings;
to replace spars after winds had wrought havoc
with them; and in general with his tools to keep
things in working order. He had a small shop of
his own filled with lumber and tools which
smelled of pitch and fresh shavings. He was
inclined to be a man of quiet mind, dependable
and self-respecting; and although children on
board were strictly forbidden to touch his tools
or to make free with any other of his gear, he
was likely to be their friend and was often made
responsible for them. He walked with them about
the decks, or in port took them ashore to see the
strange sights of foreign harbors.

On the *Eliza Ann Chase* the carpenter for
several voyages was a Maine man named Thomas
Lord, who was born in 1801 and who was a real
craftsman. He was deeply interested in foreign

buildings of every sort, but especially in the ancient temples of Greece and in the cathedrals of England; indeed, it was these which had lured him to sea. He often made careful drawings of them on great sheets of heavy brown butchers' paper, some of which are still in existence today. When he had left the sea or in the intervals between his voyages, he designed and supervised the building of several beautiful Maine houses and some churches as well, proud to make use in their construction and in the details of their woodwork ideas which he had gained from his study and observation in other lands.

Sails differed from Chips in his duties; but he also was proud of his work, and the two were usually good companions, since they shared the same task of bringing order out of confusion, or even of chaos. The sailmaker, as his name implies, was the maker of new sails and the mender of those torn and damaged by the winds. All ships carried in their holds great rolls of canvas, just as they carried bound to their bulwarks or deck-

houses — or stowed away elsewhere — new spars in case of loss. Sails was the ally of the wind, without which his work was useless. Like Chips he worked in no regular shifts or watches, except in case of emergency, for his time was dictated by circumstances. Nevertheless, he was usually busy, sitting in fair weather on the deck tailor-fashion with his knees crossed and sewing with great needles on his tough canvas. The skin of his calloused fingers was seamed and corded like the ropes of the reef-points which he set in his sails. He wore across the front of his shirt a generous bib of leather into which he stuck his needles; and in the hollow of his right palm was his big thimble, set in a thick leather band and securely strapped across the back of his hand.

And now what of the seamen, those hard, tough men and boys of the forecastle, that flotsam and jetsam of the world of ships, those wandering birds of passage, of whom many were rascals, some even ruffians, and a few smooth-cheeked, ambitious lads from New England seaports, villages, and farms? For, of all on board any merchant ship, these specimens of humanity at its worst and best were the most picturesque and fascinating; and although the captain's sons and daughters had little or nothing to do with them, for very wise reasons other than mere social distinctions, they nevertheless saw them at their work and heard many tales about them from the chief officer as well as from the bo'sun and the carpenter.

It is difficult to generalize about these common sailors, or seamen, or even to be definite about them since they changed so substantially in background and character over many years of American seafaring. In the earlier periods of our merchant marine, say from 1800 to 1840, they were principally of native stock, notably New England boys and men, for it was in New England yards that most of our ships were built and from New England coast towns and villages that

most of our sailors came. But during the years
of which I am writing especially, those twenty
years before the Civil War, many American boys
and young men ceased to feel so strongly the
pull of the sea.

There were several reasons for this decline of
interest in maritime life as a calling. First among
these was the nature of the American mind.
Unlike young men of other nations, few Americans have ever followed the sea as ordinary
seamen all their lives as have men of England,
France, Holland, and the Scandinavian countries.
American boys who went to sea had no intention
of remaining long before the mast or in the forecastle. They had their minds securely set on rising
higher, and they steadily did so.

There were conditions, too, in a rapidly chang-
ing society to influence them against the sea.
Wages for seamen about the year 1840 and later
were unjustly low, particularly for such hard and
dangerous labor. Boys who could not get the lure
of the sea out of their blood discovered that they
could make more money on fishing schooners

bound for the Banks of Newfoundland than they could on long ocean voyages. Others discovered any number of jobs in the new industrial life of the United States, in the increasing number of mills and factories. The Great West was beckoning, and thousands of young men were going to the plains and the prairies, as well as to the gold fields, to seek their fortunes.

Thus it came about, even ten years before the clipper-ship era, that vessels bound for China or the East Indies, for the Baltic or the Mediterranean began to have to depend upon quite a different sort of seaman. In the place of boys from good families, the men who climbed the rigging, trimmed the sails, and holystoned the decks were increasingly picked up on the waterfronts of a hundred harbors — wanderers drifting here and there as they were lured by rumors of more lenient officers on one ship or of better food on another. In the 1840's, if a captain could discover in his motley crew of some twenty or thirty seamen half, or even a quarter, who had been reared in good homes, he felt himself fortunate indeed!

There were notable exceptions to this general rule. Some ships still carried a majority of local Yankee seamen as late as in the 1840's. The *Eliza Ann Chase*, even in the late 1850's, could boast proudly of a crew largely, though by no means wholly, made up of Maine boys and men. They might not stay long before her masts; but they still shipped on her as cabin boys and seamen because they knew her captain as a man from their own county or even village; and as they rose to officers' berths, they still preferred a Maine ship and a Maine shipmaster.

Most common seamen, however, were derelicts, drifting from one port to another, often running down the gangway at the close of a voyage to be seen no more by captain and officers who had done their utmost to make first-rate sailors out of them and self-respecting individuals as well. They were rovers by nature, coming from a score of different countries from Norway and Iceland to China and the East Indies. In every port they spent their hard-earned money on folly or worse, became the easy prey of the keepers of filthy lodging houses, gambling dens, and saloons. During the brief clipper-ship era especially, when larger ships needed more seamen for their rapid voyages, they were often tossed on board in a state of drunkenness and complete destitution,

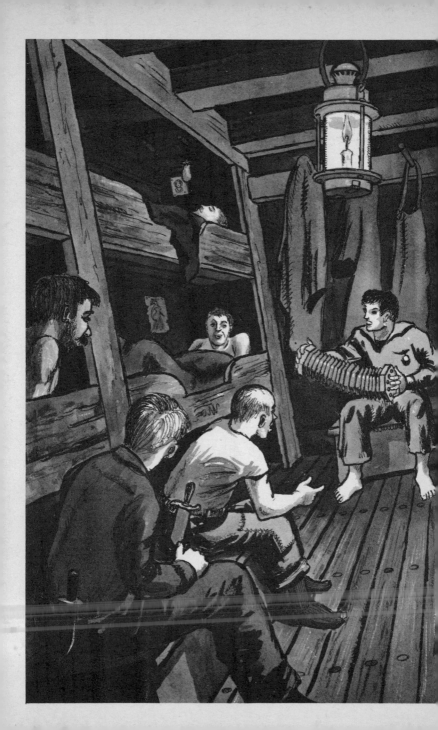

not even aware of what ship they were on or whither they were bound until they came to their senses in forecastle bunks entirely strange to them. If they possessed no clothing except what they had on, a large share of their wages went in advance to the ship's slop chest, which was stocked with supplies for just such situations. Most of them were surely no models of human character; yet, under the rigid discipline of stern officers, they were often welded into a hard-working, fearless, dependable crew; and the peculiar loyalty that many of them felt for one another and for the ship they helped to man was remarkable in view of the sort of men they were. They, needless to say, were always of vast interest to a captain's family, who watched them from a distance and wondered about their strange ways.

Their costume in port was a distinctive one, in which they took no little pride. When their ship had docked and they had received what was left of their scanty wages, they prepared to go ashore and be speedily deprived of that remainder. Then they wore bell-bottomed trousers of blue wool or of white duck, tight at the hips, a gay shirt of red-and-white-checked cotton, often tied at the neck with a black sailor's knot, a blue pea jacket, and, as their crowning glory, a well-varnished, stiff black hat, set well back on the head and usually festooned by a generous length of ribbon. Richard Henry Dana tells us how curious this array seemed to him when, determined to look like a sailor at any cost, he shed "the dress coat, silk cap, and kid gloves of an undergraduate at Cambridge" to don the typical sailor's rig.

They were always a superstitious lot with marked aversions. They believed that the souls of seamen lost in storms or through accidents not uncommon to their rough, hazardous life never left the ships upon which their bodies had sailed; and they often claimed to see such companions leering from yards or perched upon jib booms. Any death on a ship was unlucky, just as the successful birth of a baby was the luckiest of omens. They disliked the sight of birds at sea, believing them also to be the souls of drowned mariners who in this appearance warned a ship against disaster. They cherished a hatred for sharks and liked nothing better than to hook one in southern waters, beat him to death, and then file his bones and teeth into charms which they hung about their necks. Thick fog always depressed them, and a sun-dog, a curious phantom-like halo that sometimes appears around the sun, might in their minds bring any number of catastrophes.

They were much given to spending their money on tattooing, considering a sailor who did not wear on his chest, his arms, or his back some such insignia of his way of life not really a sailor at all; and they cheerfully submitted to the pain from the needles and dyes of those skilled in this barbarous art. Some of the achievements of the tattooists were anything but uplifting in their nature. Even to this day I vividly recall my grandmother's story of a tough old tar called Rats, who once shipped for a voyage on the *Eliza Ann Chase,* to the fascination and horror of the Maine sailors who were his bunkmates. I have quite forgotten where Rats hailed from, but I can never forget the pictures on his back. The chief officer first told my grandmother of them, and she once saw them for herself on a hot day in the Doldrums.

Rats, like most sailors, had a girl, or could easily procure one, in every port; and his vivid, if crude imagination had conceived the fancy of having the symbols of these various sweethearts pricked out in blue, purple, and red dyes upon his broad back. Each symbolic likeness was placed within a small square, and together these converted Rats' back into a checkerboard of birds, beasts, and fishes. One of his sweethearts apparently suggested a snake; another, a spider; a third, a robin redbreast; a fourth, a shark; and a fifth, a gentle deer. Each was thus assured preservation, even in this odd form, so long as Rats might live!

Rats has been dead now perhaps for a hundred years, since he was no young salt when he sailed on the *Eliza Ann Chase*. I feel sure that all trace of his insignificant life has gone with him except the bright memory of him still cherished by those who were children in the 1890's and heard about him from my grandmother. Whenever I see today a sheet of Wildlife Stamps with their birds, beasts, and fish, I think of Rats' back, and of his ingenious imagination which conceived its decoration, as a picture of his own wild life of quite a different sort.

It is one thing to be a wanderer with no ambitions beyond having a place to eat and sleep, collecting scanty wages and spending them straightway, and quite another to be a ruffian and a scoundrel. Sometimes actual danger resulted from bad crews, for there might be criminals among them bent on dirty work. The story of a cleverly halted mutiny on board the clipper ship *Challenge* is one of the well-authenticated tales of such infrequent, but quite possible, uprisings of men who shipped before the mast on American ships; and it was perhaps largely because of this fear that such stern and unyielding discipline was always maintained.

Captain Robert Waterman has already been introduced as commander of the *Challenge*. In 1851 he sailed her from New York to San Francisco with a large forecastle crew of fifty-six men, all foreigners with the exception of two Americans. By the time the *Challenge* had passed Sandy Hook and the pilot had been discharged to return to New York, the captain realized by the behavior of the men that he had a gang of ruffians to cope with, the dregs, indeed, of the New York waterfront. For an hour he seriously considered turning about and putting back to land; but since time and the delivery of his cargo were of such importance, he finally resolved to keep the ship on her course.

He decided, too, in that same critical hour to

pit his own wits against those of his treacherous and even murderous crew. After confiding his plans to Mr. Douglas, his chief officer, he ordered all the seamen aft, to the quarterdeck, and there delivered an impromptu speech to them. While he praised their new ship, assured them of plenty to eat, and warned them that all orders must be obeyed promptly and cheerfully, he took nervous care to use at least twenty minutes for his address. During these minutes all the mates, Chips and Sails, and the bo'sun were in the forecastle, hurriedly breaking open sea chests and rummaging through dunnage bags. The pistols, bowie knives, sling shots, and bottles of rum which they found in abundance they at once threw over the side. As an added precaution, after the watches were chosen, the now furious and outwitted seamen were made, each at the point of a pistol, to lay his own knife on the main hatch, where Chips proceeded to cut off the tip of every blade.

For some days the captain and his officers carried pistols; but after a while the crew appeared so docile, if sulky, that this practice was neglected.

One morning, off Rio de Janeiro, Captain Waterman heard shouts from the main deck. He ran
forward, seizing as he did so a heavy iron belaying
pin, and found Mr. Douglas with his back against
the port bulwark defending himself with his fists
against four seamen who were attacking him with
knives. The captain used his belaying pin with

such force on the skulls of the would-be murderers that two of them fell dead on the deck. Mr. Douglas barely escaped with his life; but from that time on the officers carried their pistols, and there was no further trouble with the crew, three of whom, to no one's regret, fell from aloft off Cape Horn and gave up their wretched lives to the sea.

From this necessarily brief description of the sailors who made up the forecastles of many if not most of our merchant ships during the greatest days of sail, it will be quite clear why seafaring boys and girls were forbidden by their parents to associate with them. Yet the captain's children delighted in the rumors afloat concerning them and in watching them about their hard, dangerous work. Many of them, too, including the roughest, were fond of children. My grandmother used to say that on the *Eliza Ann Chase* the seamen often sent presents aft by the chief officer for Ann and Abby. Sometimes they were even allowed to come themselves in his company to present their gifts. Then they were freshly shaved and in clean dungarees, from the pockets of which they brought forth the presents they had made or had bought in some port of call: a bit of clever whittling; a shark's tooth; a cheap ring or trinket; a few bright foreign coins; or a new hair-ribbon or handkerchief.

A cabin boy's bunk in such forecastles was no longer looked upon with favor by many American parents. Still, if a fourteen- or sixteen-year-old could stick it out and not forsake the principles and the code of behavior under which he had been reared, he learned not a little about life and its stern ways. Moreover, if he did his best, he was assured of swift advancement to an officer's berth.

On the clipper ships especially there were often several of these young boys, whose duties have already been described. Many captains, who either knew the boys or realized their youth and the unfitness of placing them with such hardened men, often arranged berths for them between decks, in the space just forward of the officers' quarters where the sailmaker kept his new sails and gear and the carpenter much of his lumber. Richard Henry Dana (who described his experiences in *Two Years before the Mast*), and his friend S—— were, as young Harvard gentlemen, given such berths on the brig *Pilgrim*, until they wisely requested to move to the forecastle so that they might take their chances like the other seamen.

The lot of a cabin boy was not an easy one, to be sure, but it had its compensations, particularly if he had companions of his own humble station. Such a boy, my grandfather always said, took pride in being treated like a man, made to endure the hardships and to weather the dangers of all men aboard ship. He did not expect the attention of officers and surely not of the captain, for he was there only to obey their orders. Like the other sailors he called the captain the Old Man, even though at home this dignitary might well be a friend of his family. He knew his place and meant to keep it, though he knew, too, that if he were badly ill or hurt he would receive every care from officers as well as from shipmates, and even from the Old Man himself.

When his ship neared home, sailing off the foggy shores of Nantucket for New York or passing Boston Light, and he saw her new white sails, her freshly painted spars and bulwarks which his hands had helped to put in perfect appearance, her holystoned, smooth decks, her house-flag fluttering from her main-truck and his country's ensign blowing from her stern, the cabin boy dreamed of the day when he should stalk his own quarterdeck in his top hat and frock coat.

How sad that in many cases he had been born just too late to do so!

7

THE CHIEF PROBLEM to be met and solved by a ship's captain and his wife who took their sons and daughters to sea with them was that of school. For children must be taught at sea as well as on the land if at fourteen they were to be ready for an academy or a high school. Most of this responsibility lay, of course, upon the mother of the family. If she had been a teacher before her marriage to a sea captain, both she and her children were fortunate; if she had not, she must do the best she could.

She always procured from schools at home the identical textbooks in use there, and learned from teachers the lessons which children were required to master and the progress they were expected to make from one school year to another. Then, once on board with her books, maps, and tablets, her pencils, slates, and pens, she converted the main cabin into a schoolroom for certain hours each day; and all set to work.

Most parents at sea wisely decided on a six-day week for studies, since bad weather and days in port inevitably interrupted any sea-school program. And for six days every week throughout every voyage, whatever the season, mornings were devoted to schoolwork.

Friends of mine who went to sea as children have told me how they often prepared their lessons in the forward cabin, or the dining room, sitting around the long table there under the skylight with the tumbler-rack clattering above their heads in a rough sea. From nine o'clock until just before twelve, when the steward came to lay the table for dinner, they bent over their books, learning their English grammar, their parsing and diagramming of sentences, their history and geog-

raphy, and grappling with their long division and their fractions in arithmetic just as did their playmates in some more comfortable and roomy New England schoolhouse. Their mother meanwhile sat at her post in the after cabin, to which they moved whenever they were ready to recite their lessons, or to present their compositions, or their completed sums or problems. They doubtless missed the competition of classmates, because they themselves were necessarily few in number — probably two or three at most. Yet they had the advantage of being put very much on their own; and the rigid discipline throughout the ship was in no sense lessened in its schoolrooms. For arithmetic, they had the practical help of the ship's charts, logs, and instruments of navigation, often explained to them by their father or by the chief officer; and for geography they had, to supplement their textbook, the actual capes, straits, and islands toward which they sailed.

There might also be, as many anxious mothers gratefully discovered, other available teachers on board. The officers and bo'sun were quite likely to be better mathematicians than she, and at odd hours when they were free might well prove to be of great help in advanced arithmetic or beginning algebra. They could explain the mysteries of latitude and longitude and the reasons for changes in time from one part of the globe to another. Chips, too, might be of real service as a teacher. When Thomas Lord sailed as ship's carpenter on board the *Eliza Ann Chase,* he gave Ann and Abby their first lessons in drawing. One of the girls I knew in college who had sailed on several long voyages to Australia and China in the early 1890's, when steam had almost driven sails from the sea, had taken music lessons from the bo'sun, who played the flute.

On ships bound for several ports, carrying important cargoes to one and taking on foreign freight there for yet another, there was often a young man known as the supercargo. He had charge of the ship's goods, their delivery, and sometimes even their sale. He was in almost every case more highly educated than were the officers or the captain; indeed, he was usually a college graduate, and if he chose to interest himself in a ship's schoolroom, he might well be of vast assistance from time to time, especially for any more advanced studies.

In cold or stormy weather, when to move about the decks was forbidden, there were countless hours free for reading. Every ship carried at least a small library, and boys and girls who liked to read often exhausted its stores on long voyages. Therefore, the pleasant custom of swapping libraries became a common one. Whenever they came to anchor in a foreign harbor, London or Liverpool, Barcelona or Rio, San Francisco or Hongkong, and saw other American ships lying offshore or at the busy piers, probably with other children on board several of them, this business of swapping whole libraries was an exciting one. Usually one of the lesser officers or the bo'sun gathered up all the books in the bookcase of the main cabin, rowed them across to another ship, and brought back its collection, which might upon examination yield quite unfamiliar titles. Nor was this trade confined only to harbors. Often when two American ships met in mid-ocean, one homeward bound, the other outward, sails were backed if weather permitted, and boats put out for a friendly exchange of visits — visits long enough for home letters to be written and for books and games to be moved from one after cabin to another.

The sea and the skies above it provided, too, their own teachers and textbooks. Only the dullest of children could be unaware of the stars — the planets and the constellations — of winter skies; of the Northern Lights streaming across the heavens; of the full moon rising over tropical waters and resembling some immense golden fruit, almost fragrant in its richness. There were certain areas of the ocean which gave the children any number of lessons about the strange growths nurtured there. On voyages south to Rio they passed through those curious undulating depths of the Sargasso Sea, where they were surrounded on every side by miles of drifting seaweed, great fronds and bladders with every variety of shellfish clinging to them, tiny crabs and shrimps, snails, seahorses, and a hundred unfamiliar creatures. When darkness fell over this strange Sargasso, there came with it luminous fishes which glowed among the weeds like brilliant tiny flames. In warm Pacific waters the children might be called even from their books to see incredible numbers of jellyfish, dyeing the sea a deep purple; or porpoises of bright red; or small, sinuous water snakes swimming in tiny circles, their black bodies banded with green and gold. Off Cape Horn they were sure to see albatrosses with their immense spread of wings, and now and again, at a safe distance, an iceberg of clear transparent green, shaped with its jutting prow like some great phantom ship deserted in tumultuous, raging seas.

Wise mothers assigned the lessons in geography to introduce the country or the islands toward which the ship was sailing. Once they had made a safe landing, the geography book itself must have seemed both dull and incomplete! For here before their very eyes and ears were the actual sights and sounds, trees and people, fruit and flowers, unfamiliar tongues, manners, customs, and curious ways of life, about which they had been studying on board. Whether they sailed into the beautiful harbor of Sydney between its two great headlands marked at their base by tumbling breakers; or through the narrow entrance into the deep, snug bay where the busy port of Marseilles rose, backed by its mountains of white rock and its old fortresses on their summits; or up the gray, fog-bound Mersey toward the untidy, smoky waterfronts of Liverpool; or made their way into Hongkong, or Shanghai, or Whampoa, the anchorage for Canton, among hundreds of darting sampans on which whole Chinese families lived, they found countless teachers, bookless, yet incomparable.

Cádiz beyond its blue gulf was the harbor most beloved by my grandmother and her little daughters. I heard so much about Cádiz when I was a child that it has always seemed a magical city to me, one, indeed, that I have never dared to visit for fear my early dreams and visions of it might be shattered. It was an ancient city, called Tarshish by the Phoenicians, and Gades by the Romans. King Solomon's ships had sailed there, centuries before the Romans built their walls around it and used its wide harbor as an anchorage for their long galleys with their banks of oars. I used to imagine my aunts, Ann and Abby,

walking there or riding up its steep, narrow streets on the backs of small donkeys. On the wall of our spare bedroom in Maine were portraits of both, actually painted in Cádiz when they were five and seven years old; and although they were hardly dressed for riding, each being in a low-necked dress, one in pink, the other in blue, with pantalettes of white lace showing be-

neath their wide skirts, I could never quite sepa-
rate them from the Cádiz donkeys which they
rode, my grandmother said, in the brilliant Spanish sunlight.

There were numberless things to be savored in
every port from Cádiz to Canton by all boys and
girls who sailed the Seven Seas. There were visits
to other ships at anchor, sometimes from home,
sometimes from England where they heard their
own language spoken in an accent strange to
them; shopping in crowded bazaars and market
places; odd games to watch, played by children
unlike themselves and yet the same in their excitement; in China, rides in rickshaws, and in
Honolulu, bathing in white surf on miles of white
sand. From London Pool, where the river Thames
widened to receive ships from half the world,
they might go to the Tower of London or to
Hampton Court to see history live again. When
the ship waited overlong for her new cargo, there
were sure to be longer excursions by coach or by
railway to cities which land-children of their day
could never hope to see, Paris or Athens, Rome

or canal-cut Venice, or into the towns and villages of Sicily, where peasants sang at their work in the terraced vineyards and ancient temples stood in ruins, and behind which Mount Etna sent her cloud of blue smoke into the clear air.

Always at nightfall, while the ship swung at her anchors, there was the pleasant sense of quiet and safety, about which one did not say too much, perhaps, but which, nevertheless, was there. Now there was no creaking and snapping of hard-beset sails; no whine of cordage; no straining and groaning of planks and bolts; no pitching and tossing; no sudden, shuddering impact of mighty waves. Cape Horn with its roaring westerlies and its menacing Antarctic icebergs, of which Richard Henry Dana has told so vividly, now seemed as far away as the long, impatient days in the Doldrums.

From the quarterdeck before they went below to go to bed in their motionless berths they saw the riding-lights of many ships reflected in the water, and on the shores of many countries the lighted windows of homes where other children who spoke in unfamiliar words played or slept, romped or studied, were ill or well. From such sights as these there crept into their minds, as perhaps into the minds of no other boys and girls of their time, the understanding that the whole world was one, bound together by the measureless waters over which they sailed, each country and each island dependent upon all others for their well-being, their happiness, and their hope.

This was surely the greatest and the wisest teaching of the sea to those who sailed, more important and far-reaching than any other lesson in any cabin or in any port. For it was the sea which at once encircled and united the whole earth, all peoples of all colors, all children with their dreams and desires. Those other rougher lessons which they must learn again, when the ship once more bent her sails, lay beyond each harbor over the vast reaches of open ocean with their perils and their pleasures alike: lessons of self-reliance and of courage, of faith and gallantry, of the adventures and the triumphs of brave men throughout many centuries of sailing ships.

When I was young I learned the words of an ancient Greek verse, marking the grave of a mariner who had lost both his ship and his life, but not his courage or his faith in fearless men who sailed the seas. It has echoed down through the centuries the heroism of all ships and sailors and belongs to the seafaring history of every nation:

A *shipwrecked sailor on this foreign coast*
   Bids you set sail!
Full many a gallant barque, when we were lost,
   Weathered the gale.

INDEX